W9-BLJ-298

Horses

Parents' Guide

My Horses Poster Book includes beautiful photo posters— and illustrations for your child to color. You'll also find interesting facts about the horses we feature. Here are some ways to enhance your child's learning and enjoyment.

Read together
Read the book aloud and talk about the horses pictured. This exchange helps develop your child's listening skills and imagination.

Make it personal
Invite your child to experiment with color and add to the drawings. This encourages self expression and builds critical thinking skills.

Offer options
Provide a mix of materials: crayons, markers, paints, stickers. Manipulating art materials develops skills needed for reading and writing.

Talk about it
Ask your child to tell you about the end result. This is an opportunity to practice social skills, and it supports language development.

THOROUGHBRED

A horse's ears can tell you a lot about its mood. They flop when the horse is relaxed and perk up when the horse is alert. How is this horse feeling?

Easy extras

• Set out ingredients, such as rice, pasta, and beans, and let your child glue them on drawings to add texture or create a mosaic.

• Layer different materials to enhance the tactile experience. After coloring, your child can attach yarn or fabric, finger paint over the coloring, or simply add glitter or stickers.

• Turn household items into art tools. Paint with cotton swabs or sponges, or blow on drops of paint with a drinking straw.

Beyond the book

• Have older children shoot their own photos, then make drawings based on them.

• Visit a farm or stable where your child can observe and draw horses. Talk about what you see.

• Learn more about horses by taking a research trip to the library, by looking online, or by watching educational programs.

• Seek out horse-related museums and art exhibits. Remember to bring a sketch book!

FRIESIAN

The Friesian is a strong, beautiful black horse often seen in movies.
Draw someone riding the horse. Is it you or someone else?

BLAZER

The Blazers in the photo are wearing halters, which are harnesses
that fit gently around their heads. Draw halters on these horses.

An all-white horse is called a cremello. What color would you like to make the horse in your drawing?

KONIK

Gray horses are usually born white or cream colored and turn gray as they grow. Connect the dots to finish the gray mother horse.

LIPPIZZANER

Horses graze. This means they eat often, but just a little bit at a time. Draw some more treats for this horse to snack on.

GYPSY VANNER

Gypsy Vanners are large horses with long manes and tails. In real life, they are always black and white, but you can color this horse any color.

SADDLEBRED

Horses love to run. It's fun, and it keeps them healthy and strong. Color these running horses.

QUARTER HORSE

Quarter Horses are very good sprinters. These horses look like
they are resting. Connect the dots and draw some sunshine for them.

A horse with reddish brown hair is called a chestnut.
What colors are the horse and flowers in your drawing?

A blaze is a stripe down a horse's face. Draw a blaze
or other markings, such as spots, on this horse's face.

MUSTANG

Mustangs are often described as wild because many roam free. Where are the horses in your drawing? Are they out in the wild or near a farm?

DRAFT HORSE

Draft horses are very strong. Many work on farms. Connect
the dots to finish this horse taking a break out in the field.

ARABIAN

Brushing a horse's mane and tail help keep them clean and prevent tangles. Draw a tail for this Arabian horse.

March 16, 2016 – March 17, 2016

Horses are good jumpers. They can jump higher and longer if they get a running start. Draw something fun for this Saddlebred to jump over.

MORGAN

Morgans are smaller horses that are known for their strong muscles.
Connect the dots to finish these Morgan friends.

QUARTER HORSE

The horse's run is called either a gallop or a canter. A gallop is faster than a canter. Color this horse running in the snow.

APPALOOSA

Horses are social animals. That means they like to hang out with other horses. Draw another friend for these horses.

A horse's front two legs are called its forelegs. Horses have strong leg muscles for running and jumping. Connect the dots to finish this horse's forelegs.

THOROUGHBRED

A horse's ears can tell you a lot about its mood. They flop when the horse is relaxed and perk up when the horse is alert. How is this horse feeling?

HAFLINGER

A saddle is a special leather seat made to fit a horse and its rider. Color and decorate this horse's saddle.

APPALOOSA

Appaloosas have spots or speckles that come in different colors, including white, black, and red. Color these horses' hair.

AMERICAN PAINT HORSE

The American Paint has patches that can be white, brown, or black.
What patterns and colors would you like to use on your drawing?

The hair falling over this pony's eye is called the forelock.
Glue on yarn to make the forelock extra soft in your drawing.

LIPPIZZANER

Horses wear iron shoes to protect their delicate hooves.
Can you find and circle five horseshoes hidden in this drawing?

A baby horse is called a foal. It learns to walk within hours of being born.
Will you color this mother and foal to look the same or different?

The pony in the photo is playing in the snow. What is
the weather like in your drawing? Is it sunny or rainy?

When horses meet, they often touch noses and sniff. It is how horses say "hello." How do you and your friends say "hello" to each other?

This horse is spending some time out on the farm relaxing.
Draw more farm friends to keep this horse company.